ELIO ABATINO

VESUVIO
A VOLCANO AND ITS HISTORY

CARCAVALLO editore

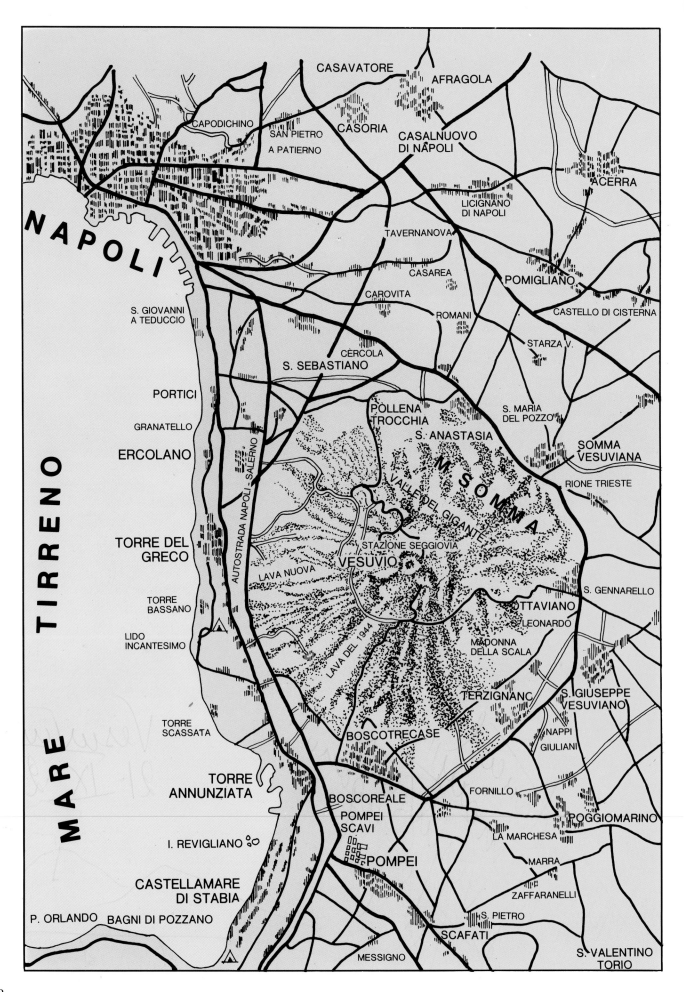

2

HISTORY

The plain stretches from Mount Massico to the Lattari Mountains (the Sorrento Peninsula), from the coast to the Caserta and Piacentini mountains. When the land sank, it became an arm of the sea and then an area of volcanic activity.

At first the eruptions took place below sea level, then on land, their debris piling up to form volcanic edifices that can be seen even today: the Pontine Islands, Roccamonfina, Ischia, Procida and Vivara, the Phlegrean Fields, and other even older areas (2 million years) that were only recently discovered when deep wells were drilled in the search for geothermic energy. The last to appear, and therefore the youngest of all, was Somma-Vesuvius.

The roots of this volcanic complex are 2 to 5 km deep within the calcareous rocks of the Mesozoic Era.

From a tectonic examination of the region, scholars have discovered that its central and lateral vents were fed by two deep fracture systems respectively parallel and perpendicular to the Apennines.

The first eruptions of this volcano probably took place 27,000 years ago, and the erupted debris rests on "Ignimbrite Campana" or "Tufo Grigio Campano" (Campanian Gray Tuff) which originated from one of the most catastrophic eruptions of the Phlegrean Fields, about 36,000 years ago. Lava flows found recently at a depth of about 1,345 m in a well drilled at Trecase presumably represent even earlier activity, some 300,000 years ago.

The history of Vesuvius is generally divided into four eruptive periods: primitive Somma, ancient Somma, recent Somma and Vesuvius. Geologists and volcanologists have reconstructed these periods through a study of volcanic products, their stratigraphic positions, and correlations with products from other volcanoes in Campania; the latest instruments and methods have been used to measure the radioactitity of these products and of the fragments contained within. Such methods have made it possible to determine the exact dates of the eruptions and to study their evolution from a chemical and micro-chemical point-of-view, as well.

The Somma-Vesuvius complex is composed of two

SOMMA

VESUVIO

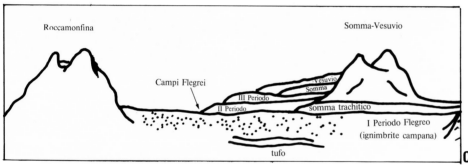

Roccamonfina

Somma-Vesuvio

Campi Flegrei

Vesuvio

Somma

III Periodo

II Periodo

somma trachitico

I Periodo Flegreo
(ignimbrite campana)

tufo

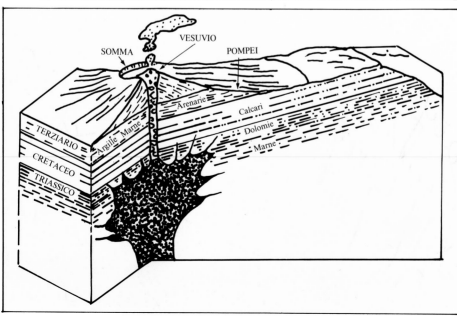

SOMMA

VESUVIO

POMPEI

Arenarie

Calcari

Dolomie

Marne

TERZIARIO

Argille Marne

CRETACEO

TRIASSICO

On this page:
A – Drawing of Vesuvius before the 79 AD eruption.
B – Drawing of Vesuvius after the 1944 eruption.
C – Idealized Cross section showing the stratigraphic relationship between Somma-Vesuvius, Roccamonfina and the Phlegrean fields, according to P. Di Girolamo.
D – Cross section showing of the structure of Vesuvius according to A. Rittman (1933), interpreted by Umbgrove (1950).

concentric volcanic structures, of different size, shape and age, but rising from a common base. The external one, formed in a earlier period, was called "Vesuvius" (or Vesvio, Besobio, Besvio, Besuvio, etc.) by the Romans. During the first century A.D., the inside cone became "famous" for its volcanic activity and was known as "Vesuvio" (or "Great Cone") and the other was referred to as "Somma", a name that perhaps derived from that of an ancient village on its slopes.

Mount Somma's activity ceased about 17,000 years ago with a spectacular Plinian-type eruption. This caused the subsequent collapse of the upper edge of the volcanic structure and the formation of a caldera, the highest part of which is today's "Punta Nasone" (1,131 m). During a later period Vesuvius was formed almost exactly in the center of this caldera and is, for the most part, ringed by it.

The southern side, destroyed to a greater extent and then covered by ejecta from subsequent eruptions, is joined to the Great Cone except for one level area called "Piano delle Ginestre" (Broom Plain) or simply "La Piana" (The Plain).

Vesuvius proper has a truncated cone shape with the present-day crater at the top.

The valley which links the sides of the ancient crater Somma with the base of the Great Cone is called "Valle del Gigante" (Giant's Valley) and is about 5 km long; on the west side it is called "Atrio del Cavallo" (Atrium of the Horse) and on the other side "Valle dell'Inferno" (The Valley of Hell).

The oldest picture of the volcano can be found in some frescoes discovered at Herculaneum and Pompei; it is shown as a single peak covered with trees and wild vineyards. In a later fresco, this one dated 7th century A.D. and found in the Catacombs of St. Januarius (S. Gennaro) in Naples on the saint's tomb, the volcano has two distinct peaks.

One of the questions which has been debated at length is Vesuvius' appearance in ancient times. The absence of lava flows for the past 17,000 years on that slope of Mount Somma which faces Pomigliano d'Arco and Ottaviano has been pointed out by Giovan Battista Alfano (1924), by Alfredo Rittmann (1925) in his *Active Volcanoes of the Earth* and, more recently (1979), by G. Delibrias and others. This can be explained only the existence of the caldera Somma (today's Valle del Gigante) which formed a natural barrier as early as then. This observation leads to the conclusion that Somma's caldera was not formed by the Plinian eruption of Pompei in 79 A.D., when it was believed that

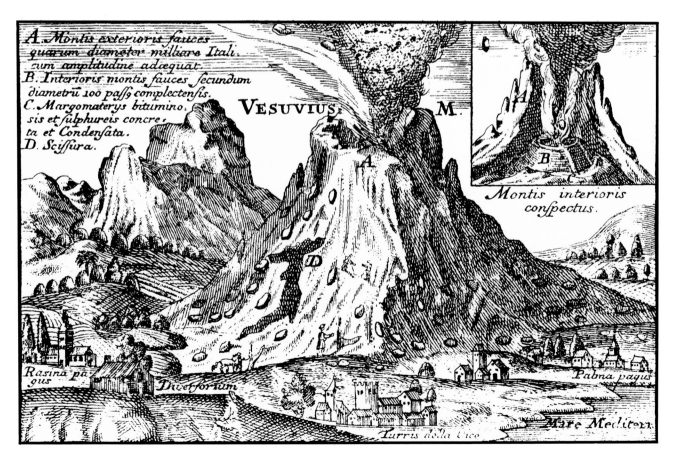

A fresco discovered in the Casa del Centenario (Centennial House) at Pompeii. It shows Bacchus with Vesuvius in the background seen from the west, as it must have looked before the 79 AD eruption, with vineyards covering its slopes (Archaeological Museum, Naples).

the Great Cone was formed, and that therefore both these formations should be greatly back-dated to between 17,050 and 14,420 years ago.

From 79 A.D. on, the Great Cone changed shape and height with each eruption, and its present appearance is the result of its most recent activity, from 1631 to 1944. The typical "little cone" inside, from which a plume of smoke issued, disappeared with the eruption of 1944. Today the crater consists of a wide chasm, an estimated 300 m deep, with a maximum opening of about 600 m at the upper edge.

Vesuvius, which was 1,186 m above sea level before the 1944 eruption, is at 1,276 m today. Once, before the formation of the Great Cone, many scholars believed that Vesuvius (or, more precisely, Mount Somma) had only one peak, over 3,000 m high, built up slowly by layers of lava and ejecta (from this the name "stratovolcano").

On this page, bottom left: A sequence of drawings by J. Roth showing Vesuvius's developments from 1631 to 1737.

On the right: A Rittman's account of Vesuvius's developments since pre-historic times. (1) After the last prehistoric Plinian eruption, the volcano has a large (terminal) caldera. (2) The persistent volcanic activity which followed formed a central eruptive cone. (3) In the 8th Century A.C. the central cone increased so much in size that the volcano became one big cone almost 3000 metres high. (4) After a long active period there was a dormant period, interrupted in the 8th century A.C. by an impressive Plinian, eruption.

Following this, landslides and collapses filled in the crater. The volcano has one flat top with a crater plain as described by Strabone. (5) The 79 AD eruption, which destroyed Pompeii and Herculaneum, left a vast, slightly off-centre caldera, the northern lip of which was higher and became what is now Mount Somma. (6) At the same time, Vesuvius's present cone was also forming. The base of the volcano is made up of sandstone, clay and marl which overlie Jurassic and Cretaceous limestone. The magma from the basin penetrated the Triassic dolomite and absorbed it resulting in the characteristic evolution of the Somma-Vesuvius magma.

Opposite: A section of the crater as it was in 1949. It has since slightly altered due to filling in by landslides.

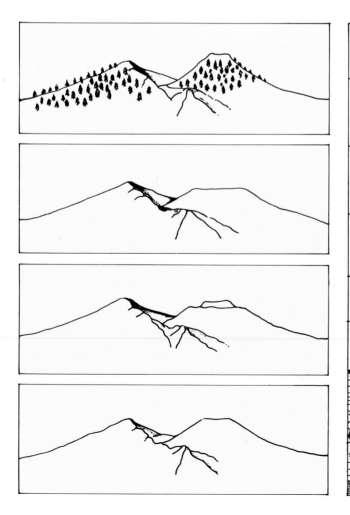

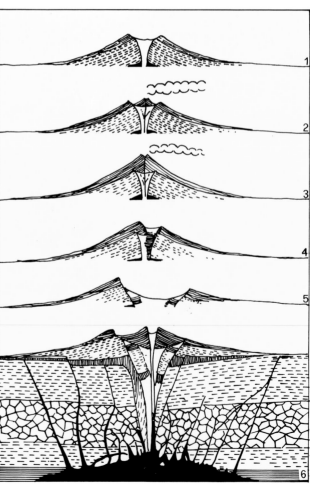

ERUPTIONS BY VESUVIUS

The first historically documented eruption by Vesuvius is that of 79 A.D.

As a result of this erupton, the cities of Pompei, Stabia, Herculaneum and Oplonti (Oplontis, Oplontiae, or Eplontis), today's Torre Annunziata, were destroyed. The locations of other towns buried by piroclastic material have not yet been completely determined: Tora (apparently S. Valentino Torio today); Sora or Sola (perhaps near Torre del Greco); Cossa (possibly situated between Herculaneum and Pompei, and mentioned by Patercolo, Floro and Strabone); Leucopetra (our Pietrarsa); Civita (situated in the midst of Pompei, Boscoreale and Torre Annunziata, it appears to be the present-day Giuliana); Taurania, cited by Plinio (it was probably near Palma di Nola, where there is a hamlet called Taurano today); Veseri (perhaps situated on the banks of the river of the same name; the source of the present-day Sebeto appears to have been called by this name).

From a stratigraphic study of Somma Vesuvius' eruptive material, the volcanic activity of the past 17,050 years can be subdivided into 9 great cycles, separated by lengthy periods of quiescence; these are documented by the presence of thick paleosols which separate the piroclastic products of each cycle. The sequence of the ejecta suggests a recurrent regularity in the activity of the eruptive cycles, each of which commences with a violent emission of pumice fragments, followed by jets of ash, sand and lapilli.

Prehistoric artifacts and animal bones found buried under the volcano's pyroclastic material indicate that this area was populated from early times.

Fear of these natural phenomena, the origin and cause of which they could not explain, led early inhabitants to worship Jupiter-Vesuvius, and they even dedicated a temple to this divinity; a Campanian stone tablet described by the archeologist Mommsen bears the inscription "Iovi Vesuvio Sacrum." But from time immemorial the people of Pompei remember the volcano as quiet, covered with vineyards up to its peak. Its wine was famous and was bottled in terracotta amphoras to be sold in other centers, as the findings of "Vesvinium"

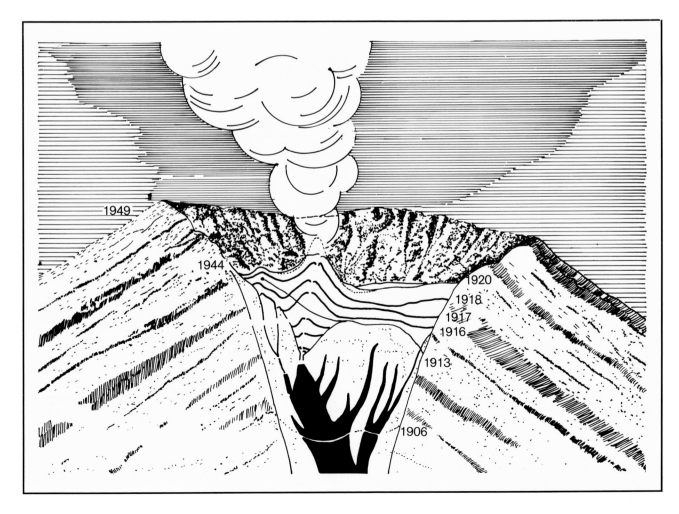

and "Vesuvinum" at Pompei and Ostia testify.

Somma-Vesuvius erupted into the history of volcanology as an active volcano in 79 A.D. The letters of Plinius the Younger, although the oldest writings on volcanology, document this event rather poorly. If there were any reports of previous activity, these were confused. Nevertheless, the volcanic nature of the mountain, recognized by Strabone in 19 A.D., was resoundingly confirmed 60 years later. Diodoro Siculo (a contemporary of Augustus) believed that Vesuvius had once been like Etna, which was active in those times as it is today, while Marco Vitruvio Pollione (who lived in the same period) wrote that "there were recollections that in ancient times Vesuvius had poured forth flames onto the countryside." The first endogenetic sign, a prelude to the eruption of 79 A.D., was an earthquake in Campania on February 5, 63 A.D. Seneca wrote: "We have learned that Pompei, celebrated city of Campania toward which converge the coast of Sorrento and Stabia on one side, and that of Herculaneum on the other, while it is bounded in front by a pleasant inlet, has been devastated by a strong earthquake, along with nearby towns. In addition, this earthquake has occurred during the winter period which, in the experience of our elders, is normally exempt from such danger. It occurred, in fact, on the 5th of February, and it lay waste to Campania, a region which is never safe from like disasters. A part of Herculaneum has fallen and the houses which remain standing are unsafe; if Nocera has not been ruined, neither has it been spared. At Naples private houses and public buildings have fallen. Many other towns have suffered."

At Pompei there were notable ruins; most damage was caused to temples and public buildings. Entering from Porta Marina, one can see an area covered with rubble on the right, before reaching the Basilica: here was the

"Tempio di Venere Pompeiana", a temple dedicated to the city's guardian, Venus. Slightly further on, near the Forum, there are enormous blocks of white limestone, possibly a sign that, 17 years after the earthquake, the city had not yet been completely rebuilt.

A stone tablet placed by the Pompeian banker Lucius Cecilius Iocundus in the "lararium" of his home, perhaps as a memorial of his narrow escape from danger, is a document of extraordinary historical interest. Two bas-reliefs show the earth rising and statues, arches, columns and facades shaking and collapsing. The first historical documents of Vesuvius' volcanic activity date after the eruption of 79 A.D. Although many believe that the first modelling of the present-day Great Cone was a result of the eruption that destroyed Pompei, no proof is offered and recent studies indicate that it is rather improbable. Nevertheless, the activity of Vesuvius itself is dated from this period and thus covers 19 centuries. The first 16 of these are not well documented; only the dates of a number of eruptions are known, not the kind of activity that accompanied them.

The Eruption of 79 A.D.

The eruption started on August 24 in the year 79 A.D., although the discovery of fresh olives in the houses of Pompei would seem to indicate the month of October. Plinius the Younger vividly described the eruption in his letters to Tacitus; here are some excerpts: "My uncle (Plinius the Elder) was at Miseno, in command of the fleet. The 9th day, before the 7th hour (noon), my mother pointed out to me a cloud that had appeared, of an extraordinary size and aspect (...) (we could not see clearly from which mountain, as we were observing from afar, and later we were informed that it was Vesuvius); a pine tree indicates its form and appearance

better than anything else. In fact, rising straight up like a very long trunk, it spread and then branched: I believe because pushed first upward by an impetuous puff and then dropped back on itself when this abated, or beaten by its own weight; then it faded away as it spread out: at times white, at times dark and spotted, depending on whether it had blown up earth or ashes.

"At the same time ashes began to shower on us, not yet thickly; I turned and saw behind me a thick cloud that pressed upon us like a river, flooding the ground. Let's go back, I said to my mother, while we can still see, so that we will not be taken unawares along the way, and crushed by the crowds of people that come from behind. As soon as we sat down, night fell; not a cloudy, moonless night, but as if in a closed room when the lights are out. We could hear the moaning of women, the wailing of children, the shouting of husbands; sons cried out for their fathers, fathers for their sons, spouses for their spouses; some grieved for themselves, others for their families; there were those who, afraid of death, cried out for it (...).

"Finally it cleared a bit; nevertheless it did not seem day to us, but rather the foreboding of a nearby fire; only the fire did not come, instead there was new darkness and a new cloud of thick ash. Getting up every once and awhile, we shook the ashes off, otherwise we would have been not merely covered, but buried, by them. Fear was prevalent, for the earthquake continued and many lunatics, with their inauspicious predictions, made a joke of their own misfortune and that of others. It had already been day for an hour; yet the light was uncertain and growing almost dim". *(Epistolae*, Book VI, 16 and 20). The eruption lasted three days, the sky was clear again on the 26th. Pompei was covered by 7 meters of ashes and lapilli, Herculaneum by a mud flow (*lahar*) 15 – 25 m thick; more than 2,000 lives had been lost.

Recent hypotheses regarding the eruption of 79 A.D.

H.P. Sheridan recently reconstructed a model of the Vesuvius eruption of 79 A.D., based on geological data from the study of volcanic products present on the slopes of Mount Somma-Vesuvius, and on the historical information provided by Plinius the Younger, as well as on the most up-to-date studies. The dynamics of the eruptions, also illustrated by a diagram, may be explained as follows:

(a) During the volcano's long quiescent phase, both the viscosity and the gas content of the magma increased due to the differentiation produced by slow, continuous cooling. A thick impermeable crust of solidified magma prevented contact between the magma (within the magmatic chamber at a depth of 2-5 km in the carbonate formations) and the groundwater, which was of meteoric origin and contained in the limestone. When the pressure of the gases inside the chamber became greater than the load of the rocks above, the eruption began. Meanwhile, with the conduit open, the pressure suddenly lessened, and the resulting expansion of gases in the viscous mass produced violent esplosions. Thus the "volcanic pine" (Plinian eruptive column) was formed; the violence of the explosions split and shattered the impermeable crust inside the magmatic chamber, but the groundwater (of meteoric origin) contained and circulating in the limestone could not penetrate it because of the enormous pressure of the gases still present therein.

The first phase of the eruption ended when there was no further pressure from the gases that had accumulated in the magma and that had shot ash, pumice, solid blocks and scoriae mixed with gas more than 17 km into the air. No longer held up by the pressure of the gas, this material began to fall and buried almost all of Pompei in just a few hours, while flows of finer ash and water devastated Herculaneum and other towns on the slopes of Vesuvius.

(b) Activity at the mouth of the crater greatly diminished now that the upper part of the magmatic chamber had been emptied.

Once the eruption ceased, many inhabitants of Pompei, possibly thieves among them, returned to the city, which was by now almost totally buried. Meanwhile the groundwater circulating deep within the limestone flowed into the magmatic chamber for about 10 hours; during that time it appeared that the eruption had ceased.

(c) During the final phase the eruption recommenced with violence (at 6:00 a.m., Aug. 25), when water which had filtered into the partially empty chamber came into contact with the magma there. This produced an extremely strong increase in pressure within the chamber; the volcano swelled and rose up. The entire gulf shoreline shifted. The volcano spewed a new, violent cloud consisting not only of magma but principally of products of a "freato-magmatic" process.

Catastrophic piroclastic surges, i.e. explosions on the surface of overheated, high-energy steam, formed a ring-like cloud of gases and ash around the center of the esplosion. The ring spread out horizontally with the destructive speed of a hurricane, descending the slopes of Vesuvius and destroying everything in its path in just a few minutes.

Those people and animals in Pompei that did not flee died from suffocation, due to the high temperature of the clouds of overheated steam mixed with piroclastic material and other toxic fumes.

The eruption ceased in less than 24 hours, after having completely destroyed the city and ruined the fertile countryside, which was burned by strong acid rains where not covered in a blanket of ash.

Eruptive activity after 79 A.D.

Little can be known about Vesuvius' activity between 79 and 1631 from the scarse and not always reliable information available. It is believed that it was characterized by prevalently explosive eruptions, even though there were also some effusive ones, with considerable intervals of inactivity, sometimes lasting for centuries.

Memorable eruptions were the esplosive one of 203, with blasts that could be heard even at Capua, and those of 472 and 512 which were preceded by strong earthquakes and characterized by lava flows and giant incandescent clouds of ash that were carried as far as Costantinopoli.

One of the better-documented eruptions was that of 685: there were earthquakes, devastating emissions of ash, and an outflow of lava that reached the sea. The eruption of 787 was one of the most typical: the characteristic "pine" of steam and of glowing scoriae was formed, and the lava reached a distance of 6 miles from the crater, producing notable destruction.

Documents regarding the 10th - and 11th-century eruptions offer little detailed information about their size and nature. On the other hand, many particulars of the eruption on May 20, 1139 are available: Vesuvius erupted lava for 8 days and then, for another 30 days, reddish ashes that reached Salerno, Capua and Naples. Although there is no document that supports his hypothesis, Arcangelo Scacchi assumes that it was in this period that the eccentric orefices named Viulo and Fosso della Monaca (Nun's Ditch) were opened.

There is little information regarding Vesuvius' activity following 1139. The volcano probably first passed through a "Strombolian phase" and then into a period of complete quiescence. During this time the mountain was cultivated almost right up to its summit, and the walls inside the crater were covered with oaks, holm-oaks, elms and other trees.

The quiescent phase lasted until December 16, 1631, when a catastrophic eruption, preceded by several earthquakes, destroyed almost all the villages at the foot of the volcano, and caused an estimated 4,000 deaths. This eruption marks the beginning of the true and absorbing history of Vesuvius, documented by reports, descriptions, wood and copper etchings by numerous scholars. It is commemorated by the Fontana della Sirena or Spina Corona (Fountain of the Mermaid, or the Crown of Thorns) near the University of Naples.

The Eruption of 1631

During 130 years of quiescence, vegetation had covered the volcano's slopes, and numerous dwellings had been built up to the Atrio del Cavallo, where crops had been planted. Then Vesuvius awoke. From July to December 1631, earthquakes shook the volcano. In December wells went dry and farm animals cried out in the night. On the morning of December 6, some farmers saw a strange cloud cross the top of the crater.

Suddenly, strong explosions spewed shreds of molten lava, and clouds of ash formed a pine-shaped umbrella above the volcano. The air darkened around the glowing volcano. Around 11:00 a.m. a few fissures opened in the Great Cone's northern base, and lava gushed out, sweeping into the Atrio del Cavallo. Gusts of toxic gases began to spread; 40,000 panic-stricken inhabitants looked to Naples for shelter.

Strong tremors threatened homes during the nights of December 16 and 17. The next morning at 7:00, a formidable explosion blew off the top of the volcano. Gigantic blocks were hurled 50 meters or more into the air. At 9:00 a.m., an impressive mud flow descended the western slope of Vesuvius, destroying many villages and reaching the sea. At the same time a strong earthquake produced three deep fractures. At 10:00 and 11:00 a.m., lava flowed out of two radial fractures on the western and southwestern sides of the volcano,

advancing 3 kilometers an hour; Portici and Herculaneum were quickly buried; the same end was in store for Scala and the western part of Torre del Greco. A stream of lava coming from the southwest divided in two and then swallowed up the area between Camaldoli della Torre and Torre Annunziata, ending in the sea.

At noon it seemed nighttime at Naples, so thick were the ashes in the air.

On December 18, the explosions and lava effusions stopped. When the clouds of ash and steam cleared, the inhabitants saw that Vesuvius was 168 m lower than before. Activity continued until the beginning of 1632 with some small earth tremors and puffs of ash. Four thousand people and six thousand farm animals lost their lives; Boscotrecase, Torre Annunziata, Torre del Greco, Herculaneum and Portici were either damaged or destroyed by the lava.

Buildings in Anastasia, Somma and Ottaviano collapsed under the weight of the ash. Lava flows swallowed most of Massa, Pollena, Ottaviano and other small villages. The layer of ash in Naples was 30 cm thick. Finer ashes reached as far as Istanbul. The crater's summit now had a diameter of 1,600 m (it had previously been 600 m). Vegetation around the volcano disappeared. There were considerable topographical changes between Naples and Castellamare.

After four years of quiescence, lava which gushed out built up a cone of scoriae inside the crater ("conetto" or "little cone").

The Eruption of 1760

On December 27, 1760, a radial fracture opened up 3 km north-west of Boscotrecase on the southern side of Somma. Fifteen vents were formed, all in a line and all active; a great amount of lava was emitted. On December 29, the cone of the central crater collapsed, blocking the chimney; there were a few puffs of ash and then activity diminished greatly.

The Eruption of 1794

After a few strong earthquakes, on July 15, at 10:00 p.m., a powerful explosion of ash took place at the crater's summit; a 50 - meter wide fissure opened up on the southwest side and four vents were formed. A river of lava, flowing out of a fifth vent, reached Torre del Greco al 6:00 the next morning and swallowed up a good part of the town. Twenty-seven million cubic meters of lava were emitted.

The Eruption of 1858

On May 28, 1858, lava flowed from six radial fissures which opened up in the northwestern side of the volcano. One of the streams swept into Fosso della Vetrana ("Glass Ditch"), Fosso Grande ("Great Ditch") and Piano delle Ginestre ("Broom Plain"). About 120 million cubic meters of lava were emitted. When the effusion ceased in 1861, activity – for the most part jets of scoriae – started inside the crater.

The Eruption of 1861

After numerous earthquakes, a fracture that could be

seen from the sea opened up on December 8, 1861 at 3:00 p.m., 2 km NE of Torre del Greco. Eruptive vents were formed in the upper part of the fracture, and a woman who was unlucky enough to be on the spot at the time was killed. Jets of very fluid lava formed a circular barrier. Panic-stricken people fled. Halfway through the night, lava began to flow towards Herculaneum and Torre del Greco, stopping at the end of December. A number of homes were destroyed, and the coastline rose up one meter. At the end of the eruption, carbon dioxide and monoxide issued from wells and cellars.

The Eruption of 1872

On April 26, 1872, 20 million cubic meters of lava poured forth from a fissure on the northwestern side of the volcano into the Atrio del Cavallo and blocked all possible escape routes for 20 imprudent spectators, who perished; two stone tablets placed in their memory can still be seen on the wall surrounding the Vesuvius Observatory.

When the river of lava came to the Observatory hill, it forked. The northern stream passed through Fosso della Vetrana and Fosso Faraone ("Pharoah's Ditch"), and destroyed the inhabited centers of Massa and S. Sebastiano al Vesuvio. The second stream descended south of the Observatory; volcanologists working in the building, including the director, Luigi Palmieri, were surrounded by the incandescent lava and remained isolated for four days.

When the effusive activity came to a halt, some specta-

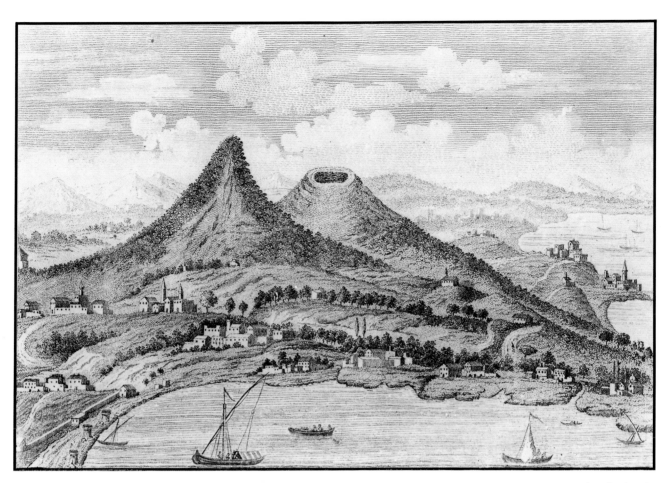

15

Below: the 1794 eruption – gouache by unknown artist (San Martino Museum).

Opposite: the great plume of ash and lapilli from the 1872 eruption, depicted in a gouache attributed to Camillo De Vito (San Martino Museum).

cular explosions took place at the volcano's summit on April 28. On May 1, the crater collapsed, creating a caldera, and the volcano entered a quiescent phase.

Less important eruptions followed in 1874, from 1880 to 1883, from 1885 to 1886, from 1891 to 1894, from 1895 to 1899 (when Colle Umberto, "Humbert Hill", 888 m., arose).

The Eruption of 1906

On May 27, 1905, slow subterminal effusions occurred accompanied by strong steam activity in the center. Shreds of lava were shot forth on April 1, 1906. The eruption was divided into three phases.

The *first phase*, characterized by mixed activity, lasted from April 4 to 8. On the morning of April 4, lava started to flow from a fracture which had opened up on the south side, at a rather high point on the Great Cone. During the night of April 4, the fracture grew wider; towards midnight a stream of lava at an estimated 1050°C in temperature poured forth.

On the 6th and 7th of the same month, the mountain sides cracked at a height of 600 m and two streams of lava, respectively 200 m and 50 m wide, issued forth. These destroyed Boscotrecase (an estimated 100 homes in the suburbs of Oratorio were destroyed, and one stream penetrated St. Anna's Church) and came to a halt 10 m from the cemetery at Torre Annunziata (April 8, 1906). During this period the central crater was the site of explosive activity that grew strong during the night of April 8. A considerable quantity of ashes and ejecta fell on Ottaviano and S. Giuseppe Vesuviano; the ashes reached a thickness of 1.25 m, causing the collapse of numerous buildings and preventing farming for several years. The vault of the parochial church at S. Giuseppe Vesuviano collapsed, causing the death of over 100 people.

The *second phase*, consisting mostly of gas emissions, took place on April 8. The mountain shook severely at increasingly shorter intervals. During the night of the 8th, at 3:30 a.m., a "fountain" of gas and lava of

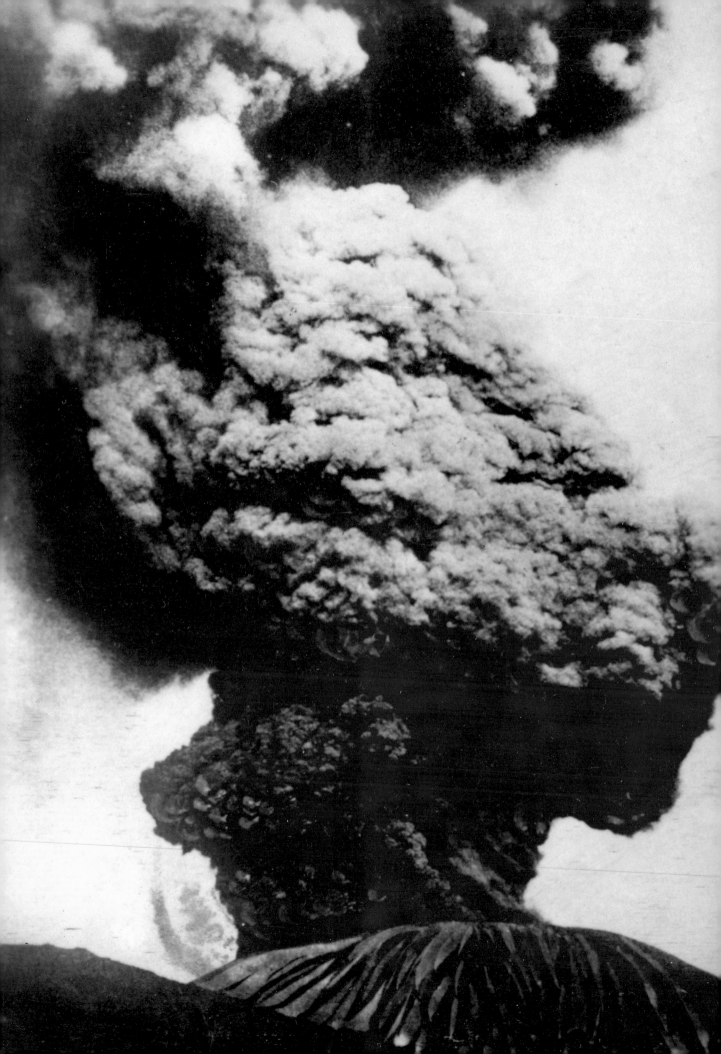

On the next page: outburst of ash and sand during the April 1906 eruption.
On this page, from the top: the small, final degasification cone of the large volcanic cone; a jet of lava issuing from a new eruptive vent; the small central cone during the 1933 eruption (Carcavallo Brothers' Photo Archives).

immense energy spurted from the crater, reaching a height of 600 m. After midday the ashes went as high as 13,000 meters. Flashes of light crossed the plumes of dust; the gases reached a speed of 500 m per second and a temperature of 400° C. The total volume of gas emitted was 3,600 cubic kilometers. This incredible force eroded the walls of the crater, which collapsed. This phase, the climax of the eruption, lasted 18 hours. The *third* and final phase, took place from April 9 - 22 and was characterized above all by explosions of ash. On the 13th and 14th, the cone of Vesuvius was covered in white ash, rich in sulphates. The inhabitants around believed it had snowed. So much ash accumulated on the sides of the volcano that during the rains which so often accompany great eruptions, they created mud flows "lahar") that gravely damaged Ottaviano.

Samples of ash which had fallen on the settlements on Vesuvius' slopes and on the city of Naples itself were gathered by many scholars, and some collected by Prof. Eugenio Casoria can be found in the "G.B. Alfano" Vesuvius Museum at Pompei.

The eruption of 1906 blew the summit off the Cone, and it became several hundred meters lower. The crater reached a diameter of 800 meters. Little damage was caused by lava flows, where as that resulting from the fall of ashes and other ejecta was considerable.

Vesuvius remained calm until 1913. On July 5 of that year, the crater filled up with lava, which overflowed, and explosions of ash occurred at the summit. Active and quiescent phases alternated up until the year 1929.

The Eruption of 1929

On June 2 and 3, 1929, there was a great increase in lava effusions, which had been intermittent up to then. The central cone of scoriae cracked on one side, lava overflowed and covered the bottom of the Valle dell'Inferno. The next day the activity became more intense. On June 4 the incandescent lava spread and threatened settlements; the towns of Pagani and Campitelli were totally destroyed.

This catastrophe could have been avoided. As already mentioned, the destructive lava came from the Valle dell'Inferno. A small artificial barrier had been raised at the entrance of the Vallone Grande ("Great Valley"), which led to the two towns. Rittman had proposed to the authorities that it be reinforced, but in vain. If his advice had been heeded, the lava would have been deviated and would have ended up in uninhabited areas which had been covered by scoriae during the eruptions of 1834 and 1906.

At 4:10 a.m. on June 4, very fluid lava, rich in gases, poured out of the south wall of the Great Cone; in addition, lava fountains spouted several meters high into the air and gases hissed loudly as they escaped.

The explosions quickly formed a new cone of scoriae, as the previous central one had been filled with solidified magma. A great flow of lava advanced at 10 m/sec down the slopes of the volcano; 80,000 cubic meters of old rocks and ruins were dragged along its path. An estimated 6 minutes after the climax of the effusions, the explosions reached their height, punching out the upper part of the volcanic chimney. Immediately afterwards, the magma rose and formed a lake of lava 70 m in diameter in the central cone; jets of lava spouted more than 60 m high. In a few minutes the lava overflowed and poured rapidly onto the slopes of the Great Cone. The lake of lava reached temperatures of 1,400° C and gases burnt violently on the surface, producing intense heat. Jets of lava reached 1,150° C. At 4:30 a.m. on June 5, the fountains of lava became more and more violent, hurling blocks weighing many pounds up to a height of 1,200 m and a distance of 3 kilometers. On June 8, after a hundred hours or so of activity, the eruption ceased; experts calculated that 12 million cubic meters of lava and 1,5 billion cubic meters of gases had been ejected.

Four identical phases can be distinguished in the 1929 eruption, each beginning with effusions of lava and concluding with explosions and jets of lava.

In the months that followed, gases issued forth rythmically and steadily as the chimney was no longer blocked.

In 1930 scoriae were hurled forth, re-forming the small central cone that had been destroyed. The same year there were lava effusions from the crater, covering those of June 1929; these piled up, forming mounds and small hills, without ever reaching the protective barrier of Terzigno.

The Eruption of 1933

After the lava effusions of 1930, Vesuvius entered a false quiescent period; activity was limited to simple plumes of smoke of different colors, and to rare ejections of small incandescent material. For many consecutive months in 1931 and 1932, there were no more nocturnal flashes of light or traces of incandescence from around the volcano's mouth. In September, 1932, a sounding device lowered into the eruptive conduit reached a depth of 320 m before touching bottom. The magma was, therefore, at a very low level.

The first week of February, 1933 marked the beginning of a seismic phase, with twenty or more rumblings a day, all recorded by the Observatory's seismographs; many could be felt in the Hermitage-Observatory area

and even lower, with a varying intensity of 3 to 5 degrees on the Mercalli scale. Occasionally during the following May, bright nocturnal glowing could be seen, and strong explosions along with a notable discharge of luminous material occurred repeatedly even during the day, at times alternating with long sibilant blasts which lasted a minute or so.

On June 3 (the 4th anniversary of the Terzigno eruption), a wide lava spring opened up at the southwest base of the eruptive cone, and abundant lava poured out, rapidly flooding all the eastern half of the crater. After a few days this lava began to descend in large cascades of incandescent blocks toward the Valle dell'-Inferno. However, given their viscosity and relatively low temperature, they made slow progress and had not reached the center of the valley by August 31, almost three months of constant flow. Towards the end of July, one branch of lava covered and destroyed the first 150 m of Matrone Road, which leads from Boscotrecase to the eastern edge of the crater. Lava in the Valle dell'Inferno ceased flowing and became an estimated 70 m thick; domes without roots formed on its surface.

The Eruption of 1944

Reactions to eruptions prior to that of 1944 must have been quite different from those to the gas and incandescent lava which issued forth from the volcano that year. Even the morphology of the crater was different than that of today. At the edge the Great Cone, inside the crater, there was a small cone from which gases escaped normally. It appears that it was the collapse of this cone and the consequent blocking of the duct that paved the way for the eruptive phase, characterized by showy lava flows pouring directly out of the terminal vent.

On March, 1944, instruments provided the first data indicating an imminent eruption; the seismographs showed a decrease in harmonic waves and the appearance of "spasmodic shocks" due to a fault which had opened up in the depths of the magma basin. At the same time the level of magma in the chimney fell and jets of lava weakened.

On March 11, one part of the central cone of scoriae collapsed into the empty chimney. A series of explosions and collapses took place in the cone. During the

23

evening of March 17, activity ceased completely.

At 2:00 p.m. on March 18, seismic activity increased; two hours later the chimney opened up with powerful explosions followed by streams of lava. The crater was filled with molten lava which then overflowed for three days, forming a number of streams.

The largest stream covered the bottom of the Atrio del Cavallo and flowed down the valley between the Observatory hill and the western edge of Somma. It travelled at a speed of 100 m/hr, and its viscosity was 9×10^4 "poises". On March 21, the town of S. Sebastiano al Vesuvio and the village of Massa were destroyed. A small stream made its way down the volcano's western slope, swallowed up the cableway and passed over the tracks of the old rack-railway. A third stream flowed southward. During this period extremely violent explosions took place in the central crater.

The Allied Military Government worked hard to bring help to the people living in the area, already hard-pressed by the war. *Final report on the Vesuvius emergency operation*, a pamphlet printed in English and distributed by the Allied Armed Forces, describes the eruption and contains a few pictures of the destruction it brought about; its aim was to inform and reassure troops regarding the eruption and to thank those who had taken part in the emergency operation. Almost no one in Naples managed to take any pictures of the event, as photographic material was not being sold to the public. Prof. Giuseppe Imbò succeeded in obtaining an 8-frame roll of film from some soldiers (apparently with help from Prof. Antonio Parascandola) and used it to shoot pictures of the most important moments of the eruption.

Only in 1970 did Prof. Imbò, at that time director of the Vesuvius Observatory and of the Institute of Earth Physics at the University of Naples, manage to get ahold of photographic material regarding this eruption which had been preserved in the military war archives of the Allied Command.

The *first phase* of the eruption (which commenced 4:00 p.m. on March 18) ended at 5:00 p.m. on March 21.

In the *second* "lava-fountain" *phase*, jets of magma rose violently and repeatedly to more than one km. in the air. This phase started abruptly at 5:00 p.m. on March 21 and ceased at 12 noon the next day. The ejecta, which were hurled to heights as high as 5 km, were pushed southeast by the wind and fell onto the area around Angri and Pagani, more than 16 km away. There were eight distinct jets, each of which lasted less than an hour, except the final one which lasted for over five hours.

The *third* "mixed explosion" *phase* started at 12 noon on March 22. These was no pause in activity, but the explosions had different characteristics. The projected matter was dark and glowing, and the quantity of ash was ever increasing. The ashes formed pine-shaped clouds and rose in wide spirals to an altitude of at least 5 km; they were conveyed a considerable distance away by the winds, and fine ashes fell as far as 500 km away, in Albania.

The *fourth* "seismic-explosive" *phase* took place from 2:00 p.m. on March 23 to March 29; intermittent

seismic and explosive activity took place, steadily diminishing in intensity until it stopped altogether. Isolated seismic activity continued with intermittent frequency for a year following the eruption, and finally ceased, at least as a regular occurrence.

As in 1906, a gaping crater was created after the paroxysmal phase of the 1944 eruption; it is still visible today. At first it was 300 m deep, with an estimated volume of 25 million cubic meters, slightly less than a third of that formed in 1906. The same phenomena that had occurred from 1906 to 1913 were repeated, thus confirming the particular characteristics of Vesuvius' eruptive activity. At the bottom of the crater the remaining orefice, slightly active, was blocked on April 9, 1944, and a quiescent phase began which has lasted up to the present. Seismic movements, often accompanied by rockfalls and landslides, occurred throughout the following years, diminishing in intensity and frequency. The rim of the crater, which had a circumference of c. 1,500 m widened, and after 15 years the crater's depth has been reduced to an estimated 200 meters at the lowest part of the rim.

Vesuvius, 1,186 m above sea level prior to the 1944 eruption (and 1,336 m high before that of 1906), today reaches a height of approximately 1,276 m.

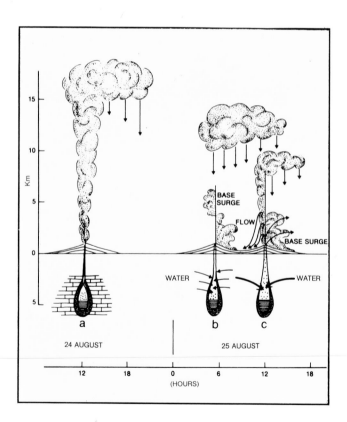

Above:
diagram of the 79 A.D. eruption, reconstructed by H.P. Sheridan.
Opposite: Copying Vesuvius's earliest tourists, two young people make the ascent to the crater on mules.

ASCENT TO THE CRATER

For those who reach the top by bus or car, the ascent to Vesuvius usually starts from Torre del Greco. Of course it is possible to follow other itineraries, less common but equally interesting, such as driving up the toll-road from Boscoreale to the peak, or even following footpaths in order to observe other aspects of Somma-Vesuvius' past activity, such as the prehistoric lava flow of Castello di Cisterna, the off-center cone (Conetto) of Camaldoli della Torre or Fossamonaca, that of Viulo, the adventive or parasitic vents of Torre Bassano or of Polena, the latter of great naturalistic and didactic interest.

From the motorway exit for Torre del Greco you follow the road, which reaches an altitude of 1,000 m. Along the way the road branches; one fork leads to the Vesuvius Observatory and the other, a bit farther on, goes to the chair-lift.

The first stretch of this road is strewn with dwellings, especially country homes, built recently. In some sections free of buildings, you can see lava outcrops, as well as banks of ashes and of earth. It is interesting to note how soon volcanic soil can become fertile again, planted with fruit trees (apricot, walnut, hazelnut, cherry, plum, peach, citrus) and vineyards, with vegetable gardens and greenhouses.

The further up the road you go, the vegetation – broom, gramineae and lichen – becomes sparser, and there are lovely views of the Gulf of Naples as far as the Phlegrean Volcanoes with the islands of Procida and Ischia on one side and the Monti Lattari, the Sorrento Peninsula and the island of Capri on the other. A few typical Campanian farmhouses can be seen, with barrel-vaults or domes, built using only scoriae and blocks of lava; these are the only examples of these characteristic

buildings that managed to escape the volcano's fury, inclement weather, and the unforgiving hands of man. From an altitude of 600 m on, you cross the leucite-tephrite lava of 1858. This is a textbook example of "pahoe-hoe" lava (a Hawaiian term), usually called "rope lava" due to its particular form, caused by high viscosity and low gas content. As it cools, the surface of the lava becomes more viscous than the interior and contorts, leaving ridges curved in the direction of the lava flow, showing that the lava stream flowed faster in the center than at the edges. On its contorted surface, in the cracks formed in-between the ridges and oncrops

of the compact lava, where a bit of soil has managed to gather, pioneer plants like *Centranthus ruber* D.C., *Helicrysum rexatile* Moris var. *litoreum* (Guss.), *Artemisia campestris* L. var. *variabilis* (Ten.) and numerous other types of spring-flowering grasses have found a home. *Stereocaulon vesuvianum* Pers. can often be found on the lava substratum. This is a small lichen with a coral-like appearance, characteristic of a volcanic environment, which populates the more primitive surface. *Sedum sedoides* (Jacq) Pan pokes up here and there among the lichen.

Below, top: broom flowering on the slopes of the great cone of Vesuvius. Bottom: a view of the thick pine woods on the hill, Colle Umberto.

FOSSO DELLA VETRANA AND COLLE UMBERTO

Shortly afterwards you came to a fork in the road; the one on the right takes you to the Hotel Eremo (Hermitage Hotel) and the Vesuvius Volcanological Observatory, 609 m above sea level. To the left there is an evocative viewpoint of the bleak lava streams that flowed down the Fosso della Vetrana (Glass Ditch) onto the slopes of Somma and onto Colle Umberto during the 1944 eruption. The hill of the Observatory, also called Mount Canteroni or Collina del Salvatore ("Hill of the Saviour"), is covered with rich vegetation; it is all that remains of the western part of Mount Somma and is made up of pyroclastic deposits (pumice, scoriae, ash, blocks of re-ejected lava and metamorphosed limestone still rich in minerals and fossils). A thick wood has grown here, where the soil is deeper and more developed; there are chestnut trees, oak (*Quercus pubescens*) and hornbeam (*Ostrya carpinifolia*); the undergrowth is made up of *Coronilla emerus* L., *Lembrotropis nigricans* (L.) Griseb, *Crataegus monogyna* Jacq. and other herbs. These plant species, the trees in particular, are rapidly being replaced by *Robinia pseudacacia* R. (Robinia or false acacia), part of reforestation efforts.

The *Fosso della Vetrana* (Glass Ditch) is a deep erosion valley, so named because it once was full of glassy lava. On the Observatory side another large valley, called Fosso Scerillio in the upper part and Fosso Grande (Great Ditch) in the lower part, separates the hill from the Piano della Ginestra (Broom Plain), a southward continuation of the Somma ridge. Fosso Grande, still clearly seen from the terrace in front of the Old Observatory, has been almost completely filled in by the lava streams of 1855, 1858, 1872, 1891, 1895 and 1899.

It is clear why this hill was chosen as the site for the Observatory building: it is only 2620 m as the crow flies from Vesuvius's eruptive axis, but is in fact protected by these two large, deep valleys.

After the 1631 eruption a "Romitorio" or hermitage was erected on the Collina del Salvatore, before the Observatory had been built. Following this, during the plague of 1656, a group of persons "saved by a miracle" built a small church named Church of the Savior in memory of their narrow escape. Visitors stopped at the Romitorio to eat "taralli" (a typical biscuit) and drink "Lacrymae Christi" , it was an almost compulsory resting place for travellers who were making the ascent to the crater, first on horseback, then continuing by foot or by sedan-chair.

THE VESUVIUS OBSERVATORY

Below, top: Macedonio Melloni (1798-1854); Luigi Palmieri (1807-1896); Giuseppe Mercalli (1850-1914). Bottom: electromagnetic seismographs designed by Luigi Palmieri.

Work on the Vesuvius Observatory was started in 1841 by the architect Gaetano Fazzini. As early as 1823, two noted Vesuvius scholars, Monticelli and Covelli, in the preface to their monograph on the 1882 eruption, expressed their hope of being able to carry out research and studies at a Volcanic Meteorological Observatory of Vesuvius, in order to have a clearer idea of what effects the eruptions had on meteorology and on the surrounding area. Leopoldo Pilla carried out such a program of observation and study between 1832-1839, making interesting observations on Vesuvius' activity and on the nature of its erupted matter.

It was only in 1840 that Ferdinand II, newly enthroned as Bourbon ruler of the Kingdom of the Two Sicilies, authorized the construction of a Meteorological Observatory and, on the advice of the French astronomer Arago, entrusted this project to Macedonio Melloni of Parma, who had been exiled to Paris for his liberal ideas. The Observatory, not yet completed, was officially inaugurated on the occasion of the VII Congress of Italian Scientists at Naples.

The Observatory is a characteristic structure where volcanologists studied not only meteorological phenomena related to eruptions (its declared purpose), but also the earthquakes, temperatures and expansion of the volcano. Today it contains only a number of historical instruments; the small museum of Vesuvian minerals, ash samples, bombs and other products, the specialized library, the prints, photographs of the volcano and its eruptions, and the scale models of the principal volcanoes have been moved elsewhere.

In 1965 a more modern structure was built adjacent to it.

As already mentioned, the first director of the Observatory was the physicist Macedonio Melloni (born April 11, 1978, in Parma; died August 10, 1854, in S. Giorgio a Cremano), who was dismissed and forced to abandon all teaching and scientific posts because he sided with the liberal faction during the political uprisings of 1848. The Observatory became almost a ruin, and selling it or turning it into a hotel was considered. In 1852 one of Melloni's students, Luigi Palmieri, obtained permission to carry out studies and experiments with his own instruments and at his own expense. His extremely

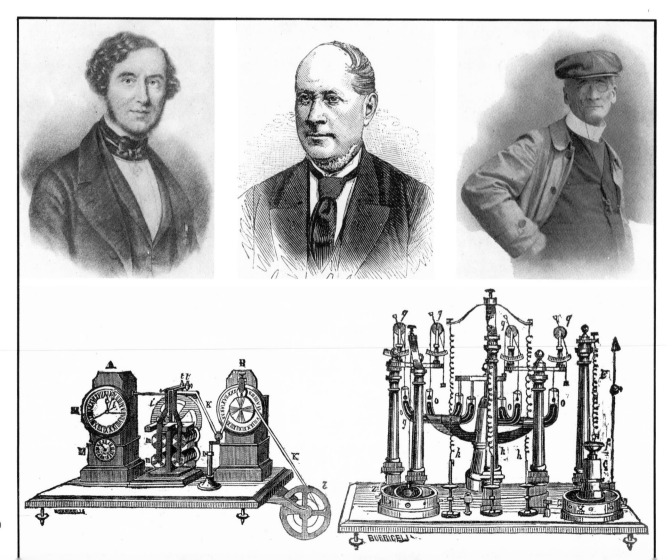

important research convinced the government not to do away with the Observatory and to entrust him with its management (1856). A meteorological tower was then built and, much later, the name was changed to Volcanological Observatory. Here, in 1856, Palmieri built and installed his electromagnetic seismograph; this was the best seismographic recorder in existence for at least 20 years.

In 1860 the Vesuvius Observatory was annexed to the Department of Earth Physics at the University of Naples. Palmieri gained great popularity and prestige, especially following the eruption of 1872, when he and his assistant Abbot Diego Franco remained at their post even though the Observatory was surrounded by lava and the building's outside temperature reached 72°C; both were believed to have perished.

Later Palmieri was named senator of the Kingdom and city councillor of Naples. In 1859 he started publication of "Gli Annali dell'Osservatorio" ("Observatory Annals") in which his goal was to provide a true, continual and complete story of all the volcano's phases. This publication continues to be printed by the Observatory.

After 1885 the scientific importance of this institute declined until Raffaele Vittorio Matteucci was named director (1902-1909), following the death of Palmieri in 1896 and the temporary directorship of Eugenio Semmola until 1902. From 1911-1914, the Observatory director was one of the world's most famous volcanologists, Giuseppe Mercalli, inventor of the well-known scale by which the intensity of an earthquake is evaluated on the basis of its effects (1898).

Following him, the Observatory was directed by a University Volcanologic Committee, an arrangement which had been used for short periods in the past; its president was Ciro Chistoni. From 1926 to 1935 the post of Observatory director was held by Alessandro Malladra, Mercalli's student and collaborator; from 1935-1970, by Giuseppe Imbò, lecturer of Earth Physics and of Volcanology at the University of Naples; from 1971-1983, by Paolo Gasparini. The present director is Prof. Giuseppe Luongo, lecturer of Geophysics at the University of Naples.

Below: Some views of the Vesuvius Observatory which was built between 1841 and 1845 by the architect G. Fazzini at the wishes of Ferdinand II of Bourbon.
Bottom right: the new Vesuvius Observatory built in 1967 under the influence of Professor Giuseppe Imbò.

ATRIO DEL CAVALLO, MONTE SOMMA AND VALLE DELL'INFERNO

Offering wonderful views, the road skirts the 1944 lava streams, devoid of vegetation except for the pioneer plants found in Fosso della Vetrana. The lava is type "aa" (as per Hawaiian terminology) and is made up of scoriae blocks of every dimension. From 1944 to the present, pioneer plants, principally the lichen *Stereocaulon vesuvianum*, have covered most of this lava. Gas-rich lava streams advanced slowly, forming a mosaic of scoriae and incandescent blocks. The rock is olivine-bearing leucite-tephrite, very rich in leucite crystals (up to 5 mm in size). The crystals and grains of olivine, augite, and plagioclase can hardly be seen with the naked eye.

The road coninues to wind its way up; "grottoes" in the lava and, higher up, volcanic lava "bombs" up to a meter in size are frequently seen. Reaching the dome of Colle Umberto, the results of the Forestry Service's reforestation work can be seen, for the hill is covered by a thick conifer wood.

The woods are composed of domestic pines *(Pinus pinea* L.), and large stretches cover the southern slope between 200 and 600 meters above sea level. These trees, which were once very sparse on Vesuvius, have been used increasingly since c. 1830 for reforestation purposes, as they grow well in the thin layer of soil that gets deposited on the lava flows or in small holes made especially for them in the lava.

Holm-oak (*Quercus ilex* L.) can frequently be found mixed in with the pine trees. Although it grows with difficulty, the presence of this plant shows that vegetation would tend to evolve in this direction, eventually forming a wood of holm-oak, were its evolution not constantly interrupted by the combined actions of volcanic eruptions and man. The pine-woods have little

undergrowth, consisting mostly of *Cytisus scoparius* (L.) Link. (Ginestra dei Carbonai or "Coalman's Broom"). The formation of Colle Umberto began on July 3, 1895, when a radial fissure appeared at the foot of the northwestern slope of Vesuvius' cone. The lava, poor in gases and of low temperature, flowed out of four vents. The viscosity was great and a number of small domes were formed; these merged at the end into one dome, 200 m high: Colle Umberto. Rope lava can be seen around the dome. The rock is phonolitic tephrite with leucite and olivine. The volume of lava forming the cone is estimated to be 100,000 cubic meters; the whole dome is considered to be an adventive or parasitic vent. Between 1816 and 1822 lava was released where the cone stands now. In 1820 the Frenchman Luigi Coutrel had the morbid idea of throwing himself into one of these vents, situated on the side facing the Observatory. Noted on the maps of Vesuvius as "Cono Coutrel", it was called "Frenchman's Mouth" by the guides. It disappeared in the fiery eruption of 1872 and was later buried by the lava mass of Colle Umberto (1895-1899).

A kilometer farther on, the road becomes a bit less steep and you reach the bottom of the Atrio del Cavallo, the western part of Somma's caldera. From the inside, the crater wall rises in an enormous cliff, more than 200 m high. The highest peak on Somma is the "Punta del Nasone" or "Tip of the Big Nose" (1,132 m). The name "Atrio del Cavallo" ("Atrium of the Horse") derives from the fact that in olden times the horses were refreshed here and it was a stopping point for passengers before they continued the ascent of the Great Cone on foot or in sedan-chair. As early as the 700's the horses stopped instead on the Collina del Salvatore (present-day site of the Observatory), perhaps because of the danger one could run in the lower part of the vally if lava suddenly started flowing from the volcano. The slope between the Great Vesuvius Cone and the wall of Somma is gentler, due to the quantities of ash that cover the lower part of the crater. The bottom of the Atrio is covered with lava which flowed into the Fosso della Vetrana on March 18-21, 1944, forcing its way between Somma's base and Colle Umberto's dome. At a certain point a narrow lane branches from the main road to the left, crossing the 1944 "aa" lava and making it possible to reach the foot of Mount Somma's cliff. A brief stop in this area is recommended in order to observe the lava structures and the colonies of pioneer plants.

From here the structure of the stratovolcano becomes evident. Alternating banks of scoriae, lapilli and lava streams are crossed by dikes, veins, and sills. From here it is possible, though extremely difficult, to ascend Somma along a narrow path (some parts of which are almost impassable and very dangerous) and to descend along the woody outside slope toward the settlements of Pollena and Trocchia.

The woods that cover Somma are similar to those already seen on Colle dei Canteroni (the site of the Vesuvius Observatory); autochthonus plants such as chestnut, oak, *Ostrya*, and ash trees are mixed with *Robinia* (false acacia), while *Hedera* and *Helix* L., *Festuca exaltata* Presl., *Orchis maculata* L.., and *Illilium bulbiferum* L. with large orange flowers grow in abundance in the undergrowth and clearings.

There are also a number of plants which are totally absent in neighboring areas: *Sorbus aria, Cephalanthera rubra* and, most notably, a conspicuous copse of birch trees *(Betula pendula* Roth), rather rare in southern Italy, on the western side of Punta Nasone.

The birch spread during the glacier age in Italy, but now these trees are few and limited to small, isolated groups in cool but sunny spots where the soil is stony and, above all, acid. They can be found only in mountain environments in the "beech belt", i.e. above 800-1000 meters. There are no beech trees on Somma, however, although they are plentiful on the surrounding mountains. This is due to the typically mesophile nature of this plant, which needs very well-balanced environmental conditions. i.e., neither excessive humidity nor long dry periods. Its absence on Mount Somma can be explained by the climatic conditions which are not favorable enough at the higher altitudes.

The other end of Somma's caldera (i.e., Valle del Gigante) is called Valle dell'Inferno ("the Valley of Hell"). In the Valle del Gigante, the area known as the "fumaroles" or "solfatara" can be seen. This was where the old volcanic conduit arose in Somma's caldera. Today thick spontaneous vegetation covers much of that part of the Valle del Gigante where the lava did not pass in 1944.

A fork to the right goes to the lower station of the chair-lift (c. 850 m above sea level), and the road continues almost at the feet of the Great Cone of Vesuvius, through an area of steep escarpments and a few "glowing avalanches" which issued forth during the final explosive phases of the March 1944 eruptions (lava fountain phase). In this area can be found enormous blocks, lapilli and ash which fell onto the slopes of Vesuvius and, shaken by the explosions, slid down together in a chaotic mass, coming to a halt where the slope becomes less steep; the material welded together weakly due to its high temperature. At the base of the Great Cone, false acacias struggle to grow among the lava, ashes, and scoriae, and there is some Coalman's Broom *(Cytisus scoparius (L.) Link)*, along with Etna's Broom *(Genista aetnensis (Biv) DC.)* and a few other species. These are the last examples of a flora which gets poorer as the altitude increases and the quality of

Below, left: a lava stream i the Atrio del Cavallo dating back to the 1944 eruption; the lava in AA type blocks is covered with Stereocaulon vesuvianum, a lichen.
Right: A piece of ejecta as large as a child.
Bottom: one of the many caves which you can see in the lava along the final part of the accessroad leading to Atrio del Cavallo.

the terrain changes.

You come to the lava streams of 1922, which can be as thick as 25 meters. Along the escarpment that leads down to the Valle del Gigante, you can see a small bunker which once held one of the seismographs used to study the volcano; right in this area small augite crystals can be found in the sand. Shortly afterwards you reach Colle Margherita, formed approximately at the same time as Colle Umberto and with similar structural characteristics. Ruins of a subsidiary observation station of the Vesuvius Observatory can be seen. Nearby, at the beginning of a path which leads down into the Valle del Gigante, another road branches off; it is interesting for its scenic views over the Valle dell'Inferno and leads to the toll-road which comes up from Boscotrecase.

The road we are following ends a bit further on in a car park, where there is a refreshment stand and a number of other booths that sell souvenirs of Vesuvius. At the sides of this square, which is at the base of the Great Cone, it is easy to find isolated crystals of augite (up to 2-3 cm in size), scoriae rich in larger augite crystals and particles of mica, small bombs, and lava fragments with visible leucite crystals (sometimes transformed into analcime) in the sand.

VESUVIUS'S CRATER

It takes about one hour to climb to the summit of the crater (1,165 m) from the car park (1000 m) along a steep footpath leading up the slopes of the Great Cone. The vegetation has almost completely disappeared; only *Silene vulgaris* (Moench) Gareke ssp. *angustifolia* (Miller) Hayek, *Rumex acetosella* L., *Scrophularia canina* L. var. *bicolor* (S. et S.) can be seen, scattered here and there.

At the summit there is a fee-booth for guides and tolls. The path, built as well as possible on the scoriae, lapilli, sand and ash which make up the bulk of the Great Cone, ends in an open space where there are refreshment and souvenir stands and from which you can enjoy a wonderful view of the coast, the sea, and the inside of the crater.

This enormous chasm is almost circular, an estimated 600 m wide and 200 m deep; it was formed during the eruption of 1944. The northern and eastern walls are made of a sequence of lava streams built up between 1913 and 1944 in the 1906 crater; in fact, the earlier crater was at least three times as big as the present one. In contrast, the southern and western walls were formed by lava and scoriae from the old volcanic cone. This type of structure can be explained by the fact that the crater's eruptive axis shifted an estimated 250 m south-west of its position in 1906. The inner walls of the crater, if observed carefully, are seen to be made up of alternating layers of lava and scoriae (hence the name "stratovolcano").

On the eastern wall veins, sills and laccoliths like those on Mount Somma can be observed. Red scoriae from the 1944 eruption form the top 20 meters or so of the walls. To the east a layer of loose piroclastic material lies on top of these scoriae.

There are many fumaroles on the crater bottom; it is possible to descend into it, but it is a rather dangerous undertaking and not very interesting. Many scholars have lowered themselves down into the crater with special equipment in order to take samples of rocks, minerals, sand and vegetation and to measure the

ground temperature in various spots. In 1979 approximately ten plant species were gathered: *Adiantum capillis-veneris* L. and *Pteris vittata* L. (near some fumaroles); *Salis caprea* L., *Populus tremula* L., *Populus nigra* L. (among boulders on the crater bottom and on the debris fans); *Rumex acetosella* L., *Silene vulgaris* (Moench) Garke ssp. *angustifolia* (Miller) Hayek, *Centranthus ruber* (L.) and *Solidago virgaurea* L. Common throughout the crater are *Scrophularia canina* L. ssp. *bicolor* (Sibth. et Sm.) W. Greuter, *Aster squamatus, Artemisia campestris* L. var. *variabilis* Ten. and *Cynodon dactylon* (L.) Pers., a grass.

White, yellow and orange-coloured encrustations can be noted on scoriae here and there, a sign that the fumaroles have had a very intense and long-lasting activity. The white crystals are for the most part gypsum and ammonium chloride; the yellow ones are sulphur and iron oxide. At times hematite crystals can be found in cracks.

To the southeast of the upper chair-lift station, 20 meters or so below the crater's rim, a few fumaroles smoke and can at times be easily observed. Up to a few years ago the guides took visitors into the crater to give a standard demonstration of how water vapor ionizes, using the smoke from a cigarette or a flaming torch as condensation nuclei.

If there are particles (or condensation nuclei) in the air, the oversaturated vapor will condense on these into droplets, forming a cloud. Due to the solid particles in the smoke and to the ionization induced by the flames, new nuclei form and there is more condensation of vapor from all the fumaroles. The present temperature is around 80°C, but it was approximately 400°C immediately after the eruption of 1944. The fumaroles are surrounded by damp scoriae where a pioneer thermophile flora is evident in certain points.

On the crater's eastern wall there is a fumarole which still has a rather high temperature (500°C). Vesuvius' volcanic conduit is believed to be right on this part of the crater. White crystals of halite and cotunnite, crys-

tals of black tenorite and red erythrosiderite or rock salt may be found in the crater. Well-formed crystals of augite are frequently seen in the ash and sand at Vesuvius' summit. It is not unusual to find lava bombs, even spindle or bread-crust bombs.

There are an estimated 230 minerals on Vesuvius: fumarolic, pneumatolitic and metamorphic. The most typical of these is Vesuvianite, first discovered on Mount Somma; as previously noted, augite is the easiest to find. The most recent find, studied in 1982, is called Caratite. Many of the minerals to be found on Mount Somma-Vesuvius carry the names of scientistis who discovered new species: Covellite, Monticellite, Ferrucite, Scacchite.

Vesuvian minerals do not have the fame, size and color of those of the Alps, and many have become rather rare, as can be seen from a visit to the splendid Vesuvian collections in the University of Naples' Museum of Mineralogy or the "Giovan Battista Alfano" Vesuvius Museum in Pompei.

Following the path along the edge of the crater, it is possible to reach the end of the toll-road, already mentioned, that comes from Boscotrecase. A complete tour of the crater's summit takes about an hour, on a very rough and dangerous path more than 1 1/2 km long; a guide is required. From Vesuvius' summit a remarkable view is offered of both Somma's crater and the Valle del Gigante, from the Atrio del Cavallo and Colle Umberto to the Valle dell'Inferno. If the sky is clear, you can enjoy a magnificent panorama over a good part of the Campanian Plain (partially blocked by Somma's ridge), over the Gulf of Naples, from Campanella Point to Cape Miseno and the islands of Capri, Ischia, Vivara and Procida; and beyond, up to Cape Circeo (130 km as the crow flies), Ventotene (82 km), the mountains of the island of Ponza (125 km) to Roccamonfina Promontory (64 km) and the rugged chain of the Apennines, with its criss-cross of valleys.

*Left, top: inside the crater.
Centre: the phenomenon
of ionization of gases in
the fumaroles inside the
crater, 1944.
Bottom: visitors to the
crater, 1944.*

THE HISTORY OF EXCURSIONS ONTO VESUVIUS

Below: An pamphlet advertising Vesuvius's funicular which was opened in 1880.

In the past the ascent to the volcano was very different from that today. The first visitors must have had to face numerous difficulties in order to experience the thrill of a trip to the top of Vesuvius.

The travellers could only ride their pack animals on short stretches of the roads to the Atrio del Cavallo, little more than paths paved with large lava cobbles ("basoli"). The Atrio del Cavallo was in fact so named because in olden times horses were refreshed and travellers stopped to rest here before undertaking the ascent to the Great Cone by foot or sedan-chair. As the number of visitors increased, "guides" or "ciceroni" began to gather in the area. Really farmers who pretended to be experts of the area and its paths in order to scrape together a bit of money, they came equipped with cords, sticks, leather straps, ropes and belts to wrap around themselves and the tourists. From complaints expressed by many writers up until the 1800's, we can imagine what confusion there must have been.

Perhaps precisely to eliminate some of these inconveniences, a financier, Ernesto Emanuele Oblieght, had the idea in 1870 of building a cableway to arrive at Vesuvius' summit; this project was inaugurated on June 6, 1880. The shares were bought by Thomas Albert Cook & Son Co. Tourism was transformed once the cableway started work. At first the lower station was reached by horse buggy, while there was a tram from Naples to Pugliano. Then transportation improved even more with the construction of the "Circumvesuviana" by "Società Anonima Ferrovia Napoli-Ottajano" (Joint-Stock Company of the Naples-Ottajano Railway) in 1890. On June 23 1898, the Cook Co. inaugurated the railway line (partly rack-railway) Pugliano (today's Herculaneum) - S. Vito - Eremo - Lower Cableway Station. In 1902 the same company built a large hotel near the site where there had once been the "Hermit's Hut" or

On this page. Some prints from the early 1800's showing the first excursions to Vesuvius.
Top: coming down from the volcano on mules.
Centre: descent in a sedan-chair
Bottom: torchlit ascent (Vesuvius Museum G.B. Alfano, Pompeii).

"Romitaggio". The hermit had been an old man with a patch over one eye who pretended to be squint-eyed and offered mugs of Lacrymae Cristi, hot sausages and hard-boiled eggs to passing travelers at exorbitant prices; given a chance, he wasn't above giving a pinch or two to the ladies.

While serving food, the hermit (or more exactly, a series of hermits) had everyone sign a heftly volume entitled "Album of the Hermitage of Vesuvius". This album (followed by others) soon became a precious collection of autographs; Goethe, Monti, Byron, Dumas, Malibran, Alfieri, Lamartine and Flaubert are among the most well-known names. Many amused themselves by writing short poems and witty remarks. There was even one who used the hermitage album to write his last will and testament. In 1817, after filling up several pages of the book and donating his watch to the hermit, the Frenchman Luigi Coutrel had the great idea of throwing himself headfirst into a fiery mouth of the volcano, which was then baptized "Bocca Coutrel" or "Frenchman's Mouth" by the guides.

Vesuvius' funicular cableway was made famous by the well-known Neapolitan song "Funiculì-Funiculà" by Peppino Turco and Luigi Denza. It was destroyed three times by the lava and was not put back into use after the eruption of 1944. Instead it was replaced by a two-seat chairlift, which began service in July of 1953; it is not used at present and is supposed to be replaced by a modern cableway that will enable a greater number of visitors to make a quick ascent to the summit. The railway line from Pugliano to the lower cableway station was dismantled in 1950 and replaced by regular motor-coach service.

At present there are two ways to approach the summit by car: a toll-road built between the late 1800's and 1927 by the engineer Gennaro Matrone, which starts

from Boscotrecase and reaches a height of 900 m, an hour's walk away from the top; and a second road which starts at Herculaneum (motorway exit: Torre del Greco) and goes up to 1000 m, an hour by foot from the summit. This road as well was built by a member of the Matrone family (Antonio Matrone, Vesuvius guide) between 1936 and April 21, 1940. After having been destroyed by the 1944 eruption, it was repaired and improved in 1953 with funds from the Cassa del Mezzogiorno thanks to the Provincial Administration of Naples, which had acquired it from the owner. There is a memorial tablet at the head of the old toll-road. This road is the one most used by visitors' cars and buses, even if it is rather winding and steep. In the last few years especially, the area has seen wild-fire develop-

ment, and now the road is lined with restaurants and "trattorie".
Coming from Herculaneum or Torre del Greco, you first enter a built-up area and then meet a few strips of farmland. Farther on you pass lava from the 1794 and 1858 eruptions, characterized by the "rope" form described earlier. But the loveliest excursion up to Vesuvius is by foot as it was done in olden times, starting from north or south of the volcano, as you prefer.
One of the most attractive itineraries starts from the mule-track "Cupa Vecchia" near Torre del Greco, and goes up toward a group of vents formed in December of 1861, when a lava stream which they emitted stopped just a kilometer short of the city center.

2518.

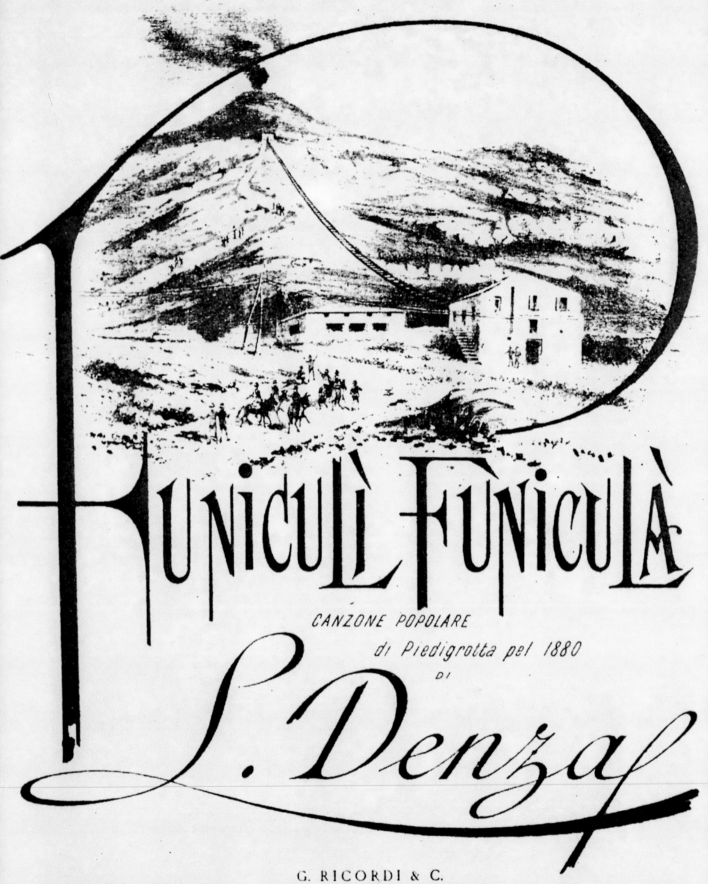

FUNICULÌ FUNICULÀ

CANZONE POPOLARE
di Piedigrotta pel 1880
di
L. Denza

G. RICORDI & C.
MILANO · ROMA · NAPOLI · PALERMO · LEIPZIG
PARIS SOC ANON DES EDITIONS RICORDI
LONDON G. RICORDI & Co (London Ltd) · NEW YORK G. RICORDI & Co. Inc.
BUENOS AIRES RICORDI AMERICANA S A · S PAULO RICORDI AMERICANA S.A

Printed in Italy   (Imprimé en Italie)

THE VESUVIUS MUSEUM (MUSEO VESUVIANO "G.B. ALFANO")

Thanks to his enthusiastic work as a scholar and scientist, Prof. Giovan Battista Alfano, director of Pompei's Geodynamics Observatory, managed to collect a great number of samples – rocks, lava, minerals – as well as prints, watercolors, photographs, oil paintings, reproductions and other material regarding the volcano, and on October 15, 1911, he founded a Vesuvius Museum where he served as director until 1933. From the moment it was built, the Museum was important for its rare collections.

It is probably the second or third most important museum of its type in the world, after the University of Naples' Museum of Mineralogy, which is known internationally for its rich and rare collections of over 3,500 Vesuvian samples from the collections of famous scientists such as Scacchi, Monticelli, Ascanio Filomarino Duca Della Torre, and other students of Vesuvian mineralogy.

In the "Alfano" Vesuvius Museum there were also 1,300 publications counting pamphlets and books, most of which dealt with Vesuvius. This collection of both rare, out-of-print works and recent, up-to-date publications was a valuable research source for Italian and foreign scholars. Thus the Museum contained a great deal of interesting material collected over years of patient research, as well as a collection of publications of great scientific and historical interest, which made up a specialized library. Following World War II, the Museum's collections were completely ruined or lost, for various reasons; only on November 13, 1974, thanks to interest on the part of the Region and of Pompei's Azienda di Cura e Soggiorno (Tourist Information Office), was the Museum re-opened to the public in its new and spacious home in the Opere del Santuario at

On this page: some chambers in the Vesuvius Museum in Pompeii. The Museum, conceived by G.B. Alfano and opened October 15, 1911, houses an interesting collection of documentary material on the volcanic history of Mount Somma-Vesuvius.

Below: some of the 230-odd minerals of Mount Somma-Vesuvius.

Pompei. Then following an agreement between the Azienda Autonoma di Soggiorno e Turismo (information office for tourists) and the Opere del Santuario in 1986, the Museum was moved to the second floor of a building which belonged to Bartolo Longo, founder of the Opere del Santuario of Pompei, and it is presently being arranged.

The collection consists of an estimated 200 samples of rocks and of minerals from Vesuvius, of ashes, debris, bombs and lava fragments from a number of eruptions. In addition, numerous old prints, watercolors, sketches, photographs of the late 1800's, all testimony regarding the most important eruptions from 79 A.D. to 1944, will be exhibited on 64 panels in the new rooms.

At present the Pompei Tourist Information Bureau is in charge of the Museum. The Museum is still being reorganized but visits may be arranged with the bureau.

A NATURAL PARK FOR VESUVIUS

Below: map of the areas where the park is planned.
A: natural park area under strict restriction. B: area
under landscape environmental restriction with
prohibition of residential buildings.

In 1978 a "Pro-Vesuvius Ecological Committee" was formed; with its meetings, exhibitions and various types of cultural events, it has succeeded in calling the attention of public authorities and citizens to the state of abandon and degradation of Vesuvius and to the general lack of interest in this natural monument of Naples. To combat this situation, the Committee has made a study and proposal that Vesuvius be made into a natural park. In the early 70's, Senators Papa and Fermariello had already made a proposal for a Monte Somma-Vesuvius Natural Park; this was part of a bill for the protection of Italy's natural and cultural patrimony, which did not receive approval by the Senate because, among other things, the jurisdiction over these matters was shifted to Regional government. Subsequently, on the occasion of a "Congress on Active Volcanoes" organized in 1977 by the Provincial Administration of Naples, a new proposal for creation of a park was made, combining ecological and cultural interests with conservation needs in the volcanic area. Again the proposal was defeated.

At a congress organized on February 5, 1981 in Naples (S. Maria la Nova), the Provincial Administration of Naples presented a bill to the Regional Council of Campania for the creation of a park for Vesuvius. Today, after years of intense debate and meetings by experts on this matter, the Region has still to consider this bill.

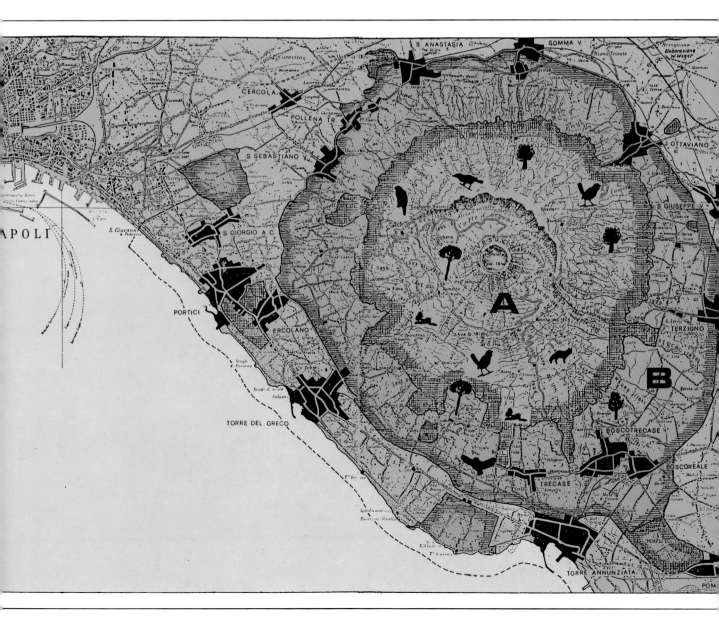

PROPOSED EXCURSIONS IN THE VESUVIUS AREA

Below: Villa delle Ginestre, where Giacomo Leopardi stayed as guest on several visits in 1836 and 1837. The building, which now belongs to the University of Naples, used to belong to G. Ferrigni who was the brother-in-law of Leopardi's close friend Antonio Ranieri. Leopardi wrote "La Ginestra" (Broom), one of his most intense poems, while staying here.

1. Motorway Naples-Salerno (A3). Between the toll-booths of Portici and Torre Annunziata you pass by the lava streams of 1872, followed by those of 1831 and then those of 1974.
2. Portici - Università degli Studi. Botanical Gardens and Scientific museums of Entomology, Mineralogy and others.
3. Archeological excavations of Herculaneum. The volcanic products of 79 A.D. can be seen along the side walls of the excavation, in particular near the following houses: Casa d'Argo, Casa del Genio, Casa del Serpente and Casa della Palestra. You can observe the "lahar" formation, i.e. banks approximately 10 m. thick of pumice and ash which have gradually been washed down by water.
   The side was also covered by a mudflow related to the eruption of 1631.
4. Torre del Greco. The Coral Museum (at the engraving school, part of the Professional Arts Institute) founded in 1870 has a collection of remarkable engravings on coral, lava and shells. Torre del Greco remains the main center for coral workmanship in Italy.
5. Torre del Greco, Church of Santa Maria del Principio. Built on the ruins of a 16th-century basilica. Interesting natural phenomena such as the emission of carbon dioxide may be observed in the crypt.
6. Camaldoli della Torre. A hill 80 meters high covered with pines, the only adventive cone of Somma Vesuvius. Probably formed during the early period of Somma.
7. Ponte Riveccio (between Torre del Greco and Torre Annunziata). A piroclastic-lava formation resulting from a local eruption may be seen in this vicinity. The lava products are "Orvietite".
8. Villa delle Ginestre at Cappella Vecchia. Giacomo

Leopardi stayed here twice, each time for seven months during 1836 and 1837, the last years of his life. Here he wrote "La ginestra" ("Broom"), "Tramonto della luna" ("Setting of the Moon") and many "Pensieri" ("Thoughts"). The villa, now owned by the University, is a center for studies on Leopardi.

9. Torre Annunziata. Excavations of Oplonti. Pyroclastic products from the eruption of 79 A.D. can be seen in the walls of the excavations. Carbonized plant remains have also been found.

10. Bocca il Viulo and Fossa Monaca ("Nun's Ditch"). Volcanic vents of 1760.

11. Boscotrecase. Leucite crystals can be seen in the lava or protruding from geodes in this locality.

12. Herculaneum – Vesuvius road. You pass the leucite-tephrite lava of 1858, which provide a good example of rope lava ("pahoe-hoe") from 400 m.

on up.

13. Bellavista, now Villa Vergara, via Armeretto, 43. The home of Macedonio Melloni, first director of the Vesuvius Observatory, where he lived from 1849 to 1854.

14. St. George's Church (S. Giorgio). The tomb of the scientist Macedonio Melloni is in the cemetery of cholera victims ("cimitero dei colerosi"), via delle Carceri Vecchie.

15. Around Torre del Greco - S. Vito, volcanic ejecta with garnet, grossularite and andradite can be found.

16. Herculaneum-Vesuvius road. A leucite-tephrite lava stream from March 18 - 21, 1944, can be seen at an altitude of 600 meters. Composed of scoriae blocks, the lava was not very fluid and broke into pieces as it flowed ("aa" lava).

17. Observatory. The Vesuvius Observatory was inau-

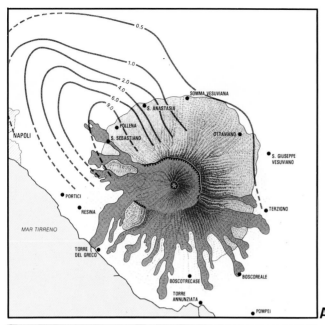

A

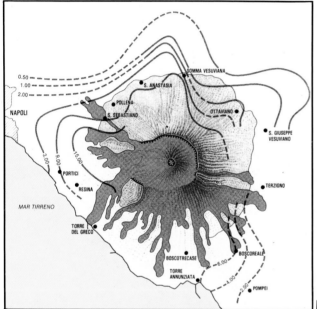

B

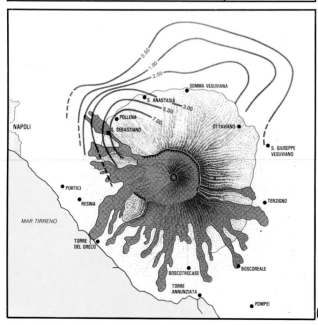

C

gurated in 1845 as a meteorological museum for arts and crafts under Ferdinand II, Bourbon king; its first director was Prof. Macedonio Melloni. Antique instruments are kept here. Topographical maps, a specialized library on Vesuvius, plastic models, and numerous samples of minerals from Vesuvius have been moved to the Dept. of Volcanology.

18. Continuing along the road that leads to Colle Umberto and the former chair-lift station, you can still see rope lava as well as some lava grottoes and ejecta up to 1 m in size.

19. The road goes on until it branches. To the right you reach the chair-lift station. On the way, looking to the left, you can observe the rope lava of Colle Umberto (a lava dome from 1895), while on the right you see lava and pyroclastic products (lapilli, ash, etc.) from the eruption of 1944 (mixed-explosion phase).

20. The square at the former chairlift station (754 m.) offers a beautiful panorama of the Gulf of Naples, from the Sorrento Peninsula to the Phlegrean Fields and the islands.

21. Great Cone. By chairflift you can reach the crater rim at the summit of the great Cone, where there are noteworthy fumaroles along the walls; crystals of tenorite and rock salt can be found on the eastern

This page: Diagram of the thickness (in metres) of the materials accumulated in three successive eruptions.
A: plinian eruption, Avellino, circa 2000 B.C.
B: plinian eruption, Pompei, 79 A.D.
C: Pollena, eruption, 472 A.D. (from the map of C.N.R. president, Prof. G. Luongo).
Next page: the spa of Pompeii
(bicarbonate-alkaline-ferrous cold spring, hence the colour).

rim. You must be accompanied by a guide.

22. Trip around the crater. Suitable for excursionists who are properly equipped and accompanied by a guide.

23. If you take the left fork in the road at Colle Umberto, you reach the Atrio del Cavallo and Colle Margherita, another lava dome; here the road ends and you must continue to the crater on foot. In this stretch scoriae and loose crystals of augite and mica can be found.

24. To extinct fumaroles. Excursion with guide.

25. Punta del Nasone. This hike is rather difficult due to the loose terrain and danger of landslides. A guide and proper equipment are strongly recommended.

26. Trocchia. A lava stream from 1944, which destroyed the village.

27. Pomigliano d'Arco. The stratified deposits of Somma-Vesuvius eruptions can be seen in the walls of the quarries around this area.

28. Castello di Cisterna. There are outcrops of an ottavianite lava flow from Somma more than 20 m thick. The lava's phenocrystals are leucite, augite and olivine.

29. Santa Maria di Castello. Here you can observe pyroclastic material from eruptions preceding and following the one of 79 A.D. There are also widespread outcrops of a mud flow, i.e. a formation of pyroclastic matter which has been carried down in mass; it consists of a rich ash matrix which contains lapilli and lava blocks.

30. Ottaviano. A sequence of five Plinian-type eruptions can be seen in natural incisions and in the excavations. Of interest there are metamorphosed limestone blocks rich in Vesuvian minerals.

31. Pompei. Interesting volcanic formations have been excavated at Pompei: ottavianite lava near the amphitheatre, a particular ottavianite lava (foam-lava) between Porta Marina and Porta Stabia, and the Plinian series from 79 A.D.

32. Bocche di Pollena, volcanic vents which have been partially destroyed during quarry work.

33. Villa Inglese, an enormous quarry, fenced off and therefore closed to the public, where numerous Vesuvian minerals have been extracted.

34. The "G.B. Alfano" Vesuvius Museum, housed in rooms at Pompei's Opere del Santuario, contains a number of Vesuvian rock and mineral samples, as well as many prints and photographs of the volcano.

Next page, top: the Pompeii amphitheatre.
Bottom: Panorama of Pompeii with Vesuvius in the background.
Below: casts of animals and people who perished in the 79 AD eruption; made by pouring liquid plaster into the holes left in the ash layer. This system, which has made it possible to reconstruct the final dramatic moments in the lives of the citizens at Pompeii, was devised by Giuseppe Fiorelli, who headed the excavations between 1863 and 1875 (Antiquarium, Pompeii).

Two pictures of the Ercolano excavations.
Differently from Pompeii which was buried by talling ashes and lapilli, Ercolano was hit by huge mass of lava
mixed with mud which covered it in a compact block up to 25 m high.